EXIT 13

A Maine Guidebook in Stories and Poems

EXIT 13
A Maine Guidebook in Stories and Poems

A TELLING ROOM ANTHOLOGY

INTRODUCTION

If you went searching for the real Maine, not "the Pine Tree State," or "Vacationland," or "The Way Life Should Be," or "Dirigo," where would you find it? And where would you find yourself, as a part of the journey?

We asked real Mainers—our kids—this question, hoping their answers could form the guts of a real guide of Maine; and, here it is, in your hands.

Exit 13 is a new kind of a guidebook, a compilation of sixty stories and poems by the kids who live here, that shows you what Maine really is.

Take Exit 13 to meet Maine's young immigrants and old French Acadians.

Travel Exit 13 to find a place that accommodates diners at wobbly picnic tables and sleeps you in twin bunk beds.

Divert from foliage tours and cruise ship itineraries to follow Exit 13 to watch bees at dusk or your breath as it frosts the barrel of your hunting rifle.

Drop off the highway on Exit 13 to dip your kayak paddle into the shallows or hear what weird objects fishermen on the pier drag up from the bottom of the ocean.

Exit 13 is a fictitious exit off the Maine turnpike, where you can go to find out what we truly eat, where we actually live, what we essentially do, and who we really are.

TABLE OF CONTENTS

MAINE NOW: WHO WE ARE

PORTLAND, MAINE

EATING AND DRINKING

ENTERTAINMENT

OUTDOOR ADVENTURES

1

MAINE NOW:
WHO WE ARE

DEM MAINAHS
Cori Myers

West coast chicks get a load of this
We got a billion acres of awesomeness
See the sun rise first everyday
See, this is the life 'cause we live in Maine

No I ain't talking no Texas crap!
This isn't another New York rap
I mean we got everything!
Four seasons, coast water, you know our fling!
Patrick Dempsey better come back
'Cause Maine is awesome, you know that!

Driving?
NOPE!
We only ride! Bikes in spring and summer time
I feel the sand between my toes
I feel the water, which isn't that cold
Cruisin' on the boat upon Sebago
Of course you can have a cabin in the middle of nowhere!

So can I get an AYUH!
So can I get a MOOSE!
So can I get a PINE TREE
Heck no Spruce!
So can I get a FERRY!
So can I get a no BRAINER!
So can I get a YEAH!
'Cause we got dem Mainahs!

Hollywood has got their own sign
Well screw them
Because we got this rhyme
Walking on the dirt filled trails of Maine
Do whatever you want because you know our game!

Eating cookies in a winter storm
Nothing else like fresh popcorn
Here in Maine we keep it natural
Hippies all around come for country folk
Local businesses everywhere you look
Local people greeting you hello
Rain and sunshine
Both at the same time!
No sharks or rotten crimes!

So can I get an AYUH!
So can I get a MOOSE!
So can I get a PINE TREE!
Heck no Spruce!
So can I get a FERRY!
So can I get a no BRAINER!
So can I get a YEAH!
'Cause we got dem Mainahs!

Watch the shadows as the evening passes by
Watch the sunset as the sun starts to die
Grab my bug spray and ride up to town
Watchin' the horizon as the sun goes down
Go to sleep as the moon fills the sky
So tourists, now you know why

So can I get an AYUH!

So can I get a MOOSE!

So can I get a PINE TREE!

Heck no Spruce!

So can I get a FERRY!

So can I get a no BRAINER!

So can I get a YEAH!

'Cause we got dem Mainahs!

THIS IS AL
Samuel Bennett

Al is a man in his late fifties, and in his face is a look of great wisdom and knowledge. He has a grey beard, he wears a warm, knowing smile, and his eyes reflect the kindness in his heart.

Al is from New Hampshire, but he's lived in Portland since 1966. He's found that it's changed a lot, but he likes it here. For example, Franklin Arterial used to be a very narrow street, whereas now it's a giant roadway.

Al currently works for Joe in Monument Square, getting change for him. He and Joe are friends, and they enjoy working together. As a boy, Al used to know Joe's parents. His father was a baker, and at the end of every day, Al would visit his bakery so that Joe's father would give him a bag of donuts.

Al was in the Marines from 1974 to 1977. He never saw battle, but he did go to Japan—his first trip out of the country.

In Japan, Al got to test drive a Harrier plane. He

told me it wasn't too hard, but he finds it the most interesting thing he ever did as a Marine.

After being discharged, the first thing Al did was to see his parents, who were happy to see him again. He's currently on disability, but he's held several jobs throughout the years, including moving furniture, being a security guard, and working in a meatpacking plant.

When I asked Al what the hardest job he ever had was; however, he said it was being a parent. Al has ten children and seven grandchildren, most of whom have a good relationship with him. His oldest child is now forty-seven, while his youngest is twenty-four.

HIGH SCHOOLERS
Elias Nasrat

The bell rang. Suddenly I saw that everybody was packing their bags and rushing out, but I was still in the class. Everybody had left. I did not know what is going on. At first I thought probably it is a break but I was not sure because it was the first period and school had just started. In Afghanistan and in India they gave us a lunch break after third period.

There was a noise in the hall. All students were in the hallway. The teacher asked, "Elias, what do you have in the next block?" I checked my schedule and saw ELL biology. "ELL" was written before all my classes. I did not know what that was for. I said, "ELL Biology." She said, "Do you know where your class is?" I did not understand what she meant by that. I said, "No." She said, "All right, come with me, I'll show you."

I realized that, unlike in Afghanistan and India, you don't have class in one place, but instead the teachers have their classes in one place. She took me into the class. In this class, seats were arranged differently, like a round table and chairs all around it. The teacher's name was Mr. Talarico.

The first time he saw me he said, "Kese ho," which in Hindi means, "How are you?" I smiled and said, "Do you speak Hindi?" He said, "No. I just have been in India for a couple of months." Mr. Talarico was a nice man.

Finally all students one by one came. Like the English class, all students were from other countries. He was talking about ecosystems and the biosphere. Most students in the class did not have any idea what these things are. Some students were sitting in the corner working with their laptops and cell phones. They were not even listening to the teacher.

In Afghanistan and in India more, teachers were very powerful. No students dare not to look at them or listen to them while they were talking. I was not surprised about this because I knew that in the U.S. students have a lot of freedom in high school.

Again the bell rang. There was a guy in the back of the class I got to know a little bit. I said, "Can you tell me, what do you have next?" He said, "It is lunch time. We go to cafeteria and eat our lunch and then go to our classes." Then he rushed out of the class. I followed him until I found the cafeteria.

While in the corridor, I saw all students were American. I met a girl from Somalia, because she saw I was just wandering around and not knowing what to do. She said, "Are you from India?" I said, "No, I am from Afghanistan." Suddenly she turned back and tapped on a girl's shoulder. She said, "Nargis, he is from Afghanistan." That girl turned around.

From the first look I recognized that she was from Afghanistan, too. I said, "Salaam," and she said, "Salaam, khodet az Afchanistan asty." She was very happy seeing me. It seemed she was very alone, and happy that someone else from Afghanistan had come to school. She guided me.

UPTI HASSAN
Edna Adan

He likes to chew gum, but he doesn't smoke. He once nodded to a drunk and told me if I ever went that way, he'd disown me. I guess his favorite drink is coffee because I've never seen him put it down. Well probably not, but he's addicted to it. My uncle and I talk about food a lot, ironically enough, in Ramadan because I know it makes him angry, and I tell him I'll only stop if he takes me out for dinner and he does.

We usually go to an Indian restaurant and the food is so good, it's almost toxic. There's this Indian dish that that we nicknamed "Spicy Balls." They come in twos and when my sister first tried it, she could only have one and gave us the rest of her other one. The dish ended up being so amazingly spicy and mouthwatering that my uncle and I ordered a whole plateful. They're crispy on the outside and have a mashed potato feel on the inside. When you try them, it's honestly like a punch in the face, your senses explode with indescribable flavor. To wash them down, we had thick, creamy mango smoothies.

Sometimes when I think of my uncle's great character, I get a horrible feeling in my stomach. As much as I was raised in a part of Western culture, I had very ethnically Somalian parents, but they, like everyone, assumed I was aware of the old Somalian ways. My uncle was the only person who had seen me adapt to this culture and honestly he was an incredibly fundamental bridge for the culture clash between my parents and me.

Every time my uncle comes to town, he gives us some pocket money ($5 or $10). My sister often would get mad at me because my uncle would give me more money than he gave her and his explanation was always the same. "She's older than you, has more responsibilities than you, and carries more burdens than you." He always spoke in Somali, never in English, another sign of trying to incorporate our culture in any way he could. My mom slips sometimes though, and speaks in English. My sister never understands why it's so hard to be an older sister, how I have to the first one to go college in America, to enter school. Not to mention the fact that this isn't my culture and I have no one to help me. There are mother and daughter problems.

I used to fight a lot with my mom because she wasn't aware of my general awkwardness as a teenager in America. In her culture, it's supposed to be the opposite: I'm supposed to grow more love and respect toward her instead of defiance. When my uncle comes to town, he not only gives us money, but he passes on his advice. "Aren't you aware of your mother's struggles? Your younger siblings are in need of leadership and the hopes and dreams you parents have for you." His maxims of leadership in my family play a role in almost everything I do. Because of his advice I've grown a lot as an adult.

Who will be my child's Upti Hassan? Who would tell my kids that we were here just because I'm an immigrant, and though we were in here to stay, this place wasn't our place? I don't know how well I could do on my own without guidance as strong as my uncle's.

ALT ED NINJAS
Haley Hildebrandt

The woods are where they belong. Black shadowy figures of the night, moving swiftly, silently, without a word they stalk. Never to be seen. If you are in the woods in between the turns of day and night, if you don't get out they will find you...

Believe it or not, they all have names. Normal names too. The ninjas I know have names, hearts, feelings, addictions, and anything else you can say for an average person. They are just a little swifter than the rest of us. Trapped in a classroom, when released, could be the last fatal mistake you ever make. They are...the ninjas of Alt. Ed.

THE HOMELESS

Jolie Semuhoza

Growing up I was taught to give
because no matter how little I had
somewhere out there someone had less than I did.
I looked at how my parents accepted them,
without discrimination
and cared to help the suffering of the people.

In Rwanda people came to my house
from the chaos of the streets,
the dust and the movement,
with shredded clothes
and dried lips
because they didn't have anything—
water,
food,
clothing.

I remember this family
that came to beg
and their faces looked liked they hadn't eaten in days,
they'd been in the streets,
they looked fatigued.
The little boy was wrapped on the mother's back,
his head hung off her back and his eyes were tired.

This isn't the whole of Rwanda,
It's beautiful, it's home,
it's where I have friends,
it's my personality.

But when I heard a myth
that there were no homeless people in America
I felt relief
I didn't want to have to see those sad faces,
I didn't want to have to help even more people
when I went there.

A few years after being here I came to find that my
myth was a myth.
I was disappointed.
I had anticipated this beautiful country
where there were no challenges, no war, no conflicts,
just living with freedom,
and everyone having what they need.
I would live without having to worry about others.
I thought my family could start fresh
and live a peaceful life.

This is the reality that I came to find:
Driving home after church was the first time
I saw a homeless person in Maine.
He was near the post office
with a cardboard sign
that said, "Can you spare me anything?"
I asked my mom,
"Is that a homeless person?"
My mom replied, "Yes it is,"
and anger filled my body.
I say to myself,
"That's impossible, that can't be, it's America,"
and as we went further down the road I had this feeling
of being overwhelmed
my myth wasn't going to come true.

When we first arrived
I knew I couldn't do anything
because we weren't stable.
From then on I questioned myself,
whether I should do something.
My mind still isn't settled,
but here I have the ability to
make people aware of the problem
and join in hand to reduce poverty,
hunger, homelessness, and sickness,
wherever we are.

AAMIR
Ahmed Suja

My baby brother Aamir's face is not perfect like other three year olds. He is a cute kid but has a humongous head—it's not normal, like the cartoon Jimmy Neutron. He has two personalities: a good personality because he listens to my parents and especially me, and a bad personality because he runs around in the living room singing Dora the Explorer all day with his toys. The worst part of all is when he sings. He doesn't sing it, he mumbles it and it's nonsense. I never thought such a big sound could come out of such a little body. But even though he gets to you a lot, he is really fun to play with. I pass the ball to him and he kicks it from the dining room to the kitchen.

One day I was playing FIFA 11 and Aamir came running in, grabbed the other controller and just chucked it at me. It hit me right in the forehead. But you wouldn't believe what happened next: I was in pain holding my head and Aamir could tell he really hurt me this time, so he burst into tears. I was wondering why he was the one that was crying, but little did I know my dad was there and standing over me when I looked up. He gave me his look that is really funny and scary at the same time—his eyes get narrow, and he looks like a girl giving another girl an attitude. I knew I couldn't protest because I would be told, "If you keep talking back, Ahmed, you will not go to Massachusetts tomorrow," or "Ahmed, you're not going to practice tomorrow."

Another day, my dad, my three brothers, and I were outside in the driveway. We were all sweating because we were playing soccer in the summer heat. Aamir suddenly ran away from the game, laughing as he went. We thought he wouldn't go far, but then we heard the car door open and close. We ran from the field over to the car and found Aamir he had locked it from the inside.

My mom came out when she heard the yelling and asked what was happening. Her eyes were wide. Before we could even answer her, she saw Aamir in the driver's seat and started to panic. He was looking at all of us with a big smile on his face. Suddenly he ducked down as if he'd found something fun to play with. When he reappeared, the car began to roll backward. He had released the emergency brake!

We all started to yell like a crowd at a rock concert. The car moved slowly down the driveway, picking up a little speed as it went. We live on a quiet street and across from our house are woods that are dense with trees. If the car ended up there, it would definitely leave some marks. My whole family was chasing the car as it rolled, everyone reacting in different ways. My dad was quiet, my two brothers were smirking, and the person who was being the loudest was my mom. She was in complete shock and was shrieking at the top of her lungs.

Our street isn't busy, so we weren't worried about a car coming, but the Acura sedan was moving fast enough to make it to the woods. There was nothing we could do to stop it. We all stopped at the end of the driveway and stood watching it like a bunch of statues. The car drifted across the road, rattled over a patch of grass and barreled into the woods. Luckily, the ground slowed it just enough so that it bumped gently into a skinny tree and stopped. My mom and dad ran to the car and I could see my brother's smile finally turn to a frown. As they got to the car, he jumped into the back seat like it was a game of tag and they were it. He thought he was in big trouble.

I figured he'd get a time out at least. But he didn't get in trouble at all. My mom yelled a little, but then she hugged him and he walked back to the house with a smirk. I thought the whole thing was funny overall, but there was a moment, when the car was rolling and I saw my mom's face, that I was scared. My brother might annoy me and get me in trouble, but I'd hate to see him roll away into the woods.

FISHERMEN AT THE PIER
Kings Floyd

Walking down Commercial Street, the smells of salt water and rotting fish are pungent in the air. Take a right, down past Flatbread's and the ferry docks, and you have arrived at what is commonly known as the Pier. It is the furthest point out into the ocean in the Old Port, and the most common place for fisherman to go. It is easily accessible, somewhat secluded, and the waters are most obliging. The natives, however, are not always.

From the back of the Pier, where the ferries disembark, the men, women, and children look like specks; miniature figures, sometimes moving about, sometimes sitting completely still, but from a distance always looking perched on the edge, about to fall. Some almost do.

The fish pull hard and the conversation is sometimes nonexistent, but the fishermen never seem to run out of stories. The question posed twice, over two days, was simple; "What's the weirdest thing you've ever pulled out of the ocean?"

The first day was a cloudy Monday with the expectation of showers. There were seven or eight fishers down at the Pier that day. The question was in turn posed to one or two at a time. The first fisherman was named Rin. He was about 5'10", muscular, with black spiky hair, and many tattoos. Korean, maybe. He had been there for about an hour, came once or twice a week, and had so far caught baby mackerel. When the trigger question was asked, he paused for a moment. He replied, "I caught a seal once. Big as a man it was, just the other day actually.

"What did I do? I had to cut the line. Gave it a fish and it swam away..." Rin seemed finished, but a woman, Sarah, cut in from his left. With big sunglasses, athletic looking clothing, and clean white sneakers, she seemed out of place. It also seemed like she had not known Rin, yet with no ill or ease she said "Hey, wait, what about last week, with the..."

An aha! moment crossed his face, and with a thanks he started up again. He described tugging on his line for a bit before pulling up a glob of what looked like snot. "Whale snot, it was," he said. "About half the size of my bucket, milky, and more like snotty Jell-O than goop." There you have it, ladies and gents, nothing gets a crowd going like when confronted with a suspected whale snot sighting. Especially because whale snot does exist.

The only other news that day was from Chris, a burly, blond haired fisherman who sat at the end of the Pier. He had pulled off a lobster boat two weeks before a King Crab, which prominently scuttled away. He was surprised, he said, because King Crabs aren't native to Maine, although can be rarely seen. Upon further research, King Crabs are generally found along the coasts of Alaska, Japan, or Russia.

My second day down on the Pier was a completely different experience. None of the fisherman from the day before reappeared; instead there were new subjects to bait. The first fisherman that was posed a question was stubborn. When asked for a few minutes of his time, he replied with "I'm...fishing... I...I need to concentrate," and he turned his head away. Point taken.

His two sons, however, were young and very willing to talk. They wanted to chat about the fish they caught and how often they came to the Pier. They wanted their pictures taken. Their father said nothing about their open conversing, and when the boys became bored, they left.

A pair of teenagers, one boy and one girl, relaxed and fished on the Pier. They seemed at first to be a couple; however, it was revealed they were brother and sister. Sarah and Tim came to the Pier every once in a while, and were very happy to be interviewed. They were both brown haired, and brown eyed. She was about 5'8" or 5'9", while he was about six feet tall. Sarah, who did not often fish and who did not know any stories of the deep, let Tim talk. He said he fished more often than Sarah, and had pulled up an old, rusted fishing pole. He had heard of shopping carts and tennis shoes pulled up, but had not seen much other than that.

"Shucks, there's been a lot more than that pulled up here." The interjection came from the very end of the Pier. A man, with a rusty mustache, rugged sideburns, and a cap pulled low over his face, was sitting, patient and until that point silent, waiting for a line to tug. He was fairly tall, but skinny, lanky almost, and very tan, almost burnt olive. A real Mainer.

"I've seen a lot more; course ya get the old seaweed, but then there's been old lanterns, t-shirts, flip flops, and starfish. I've pulled up a boot." The man wasn't looking at me, but there wasn't anyone else he was talking to.

"There's a living man that's come outta that water. Fell in with his fish. We had to sink the hook into him to get him from sweepin' away with the current." He fell silent. Pulling out a fish, he put it in his bucket, and put down his pole. With a grunt, he tipped the bucket over so the fish splattered out onto the pavement. He counted; "I need one more; fifty," and went back to fishing

Another woman then said she had pulled out a snapping turtle, but that that wasn't all that off for these parts. The man, who had pulled up two other fish, filled his bucket with water and covered it with a maroon cloth.

"I'm sorry, I didn't catch your name."

"Cause I didn't give it, honey. There's been people these past four days been takin' surveys, and I want none of it."

He didn't look like a Bill, a Bob, or a Mark. Not a David, or Frank, either. Crusty, he was christened, and so he will be called.

The Pier is a great place for stories and tales, but the question of the day gave it an experience. So what's the weirdest thing you've pulled out of the ocean?

AKAYLAH
Shaya Chhloeum

It's complicated getting her to eat; she's tall, wiggly, and skinny.
Every time Akaylah is in her highchair,
She dumps everything off her plate onto her tray.
All she wants to do is stay on her bottle.

She does love grapes.
I don't know how she does it but
When she eats grapes,
She eats the juice and spits out the skin.

Akaylah is my daughter.
She's a year and a half, she's mixed.
Half Afghan, half Cambodian
Her name is spelt a way for you to pronounce it.

Akaylah Chhloeum.
I haven't added her father's last name and if I do,
I would want it to be her middle name—
Shir, which means "lion."

It's complicated because her grandfather doesn't know about her yet.
It would kill him to know.
Her grandfather is a very strict Muslim,
and Akaylah's father is the eldest son in his family.

In a Muslim family,
the eldest son has the responsibility of taking care of the family.
He should have a Muslim wife, and if he does have a child,
the child should follow the father's religion.

Akaylah only sees her father's side of the family
when her grandfather is out of town.
He will be the last person to know
and I know it would hurt him.

It's complicated.

Last week I didn't go to school.

I couldn't find a slot at free daycare.

My mom quit her job so she could watch Akaylah.

She's very clingy and only wants to be with people who love her.

I know when I'm at school,

She's safe all day lying in bed watching TV with my mom.

I had to hide this morning so I could go to school.

When she was three months old,

I shaved her head by myself so her hair would grow thicker.

She has her father's hair, curly and medium brown, and

Her father's eye shape with my eye color.

She has light skin, way different from mine.

Akaylah has big hands, like mine and her father's.

See, I told you,

It's complicated.

A BOY ON THE PLAYGROUND
Derek Eldredge

Here I am, ten years old and fighting against myself not to cry, to show weakness against the school ground bullies. Two of the five big eighth graders are holding my arms apart, one is on my chest crushing it, his weight pummeling my face—it will hurt but not bleed. The other two are making a circle with the other fifth graders out for recess, showing them what happens when you don't give them your lunch money and tell the teacher what they said.

"Do you see what this pathetic little runt did to us, not giving us money to get food?"

The three let me up—or hoist me up, by pulling my hair to my back. Then they spit in my face and throw me to the ground again.

At this time the teachers come by, looking at me, then say, "What happened here?" They know what happened.

The big chunky boys look around and say that I fell so they want to make sure I am okay. Everyone knows that it's not true. One teacher, Ms. Chairman, stands in front of the five bullies. She asks me what happened. The five are shaking their fists and mouthing "I'll kill you," and "Don't you dare," so I look around at my peers even though I know they think I am weird.

For starters I am the only orphan in the school. I have olive skin and brown hair. I have a scar like a tiger attacked me—three big rips on the top of my head, no hair grows there. Also, the hair on my eyebrows grows and grows—it's like having two ferrets on my face but the right one looks like something ate it, all distorted and a chunk missing. Along with the new bruises on my face, I guess I look grave.

The answer everyone gives me without talking is a long look at the five boys, more like men. All eyes go back to me. I look around, smirk at the five and say,

"They beat me up."

Outraged, the boy who hit me—I think his name is Alex—yells out, "No, we didn't! He's a lying little weasel wanting to get us in trouble...look at him! Who wants to touch him? He needs to die!"

Ms. Chairman looks at me and says, "Very well, we have enough witnesses here to solve this." She takes of her glasses and rolls them in her fingers. She smirks showing her small ugly teeth, gaps in between them, small upper lip looking even smaller, cheeks going to her eyes, and says again, "What happened? I want to know now."

A cannon of fear shoots into each kid's heart. Knowing what will happen they all say, "He fell down," and "He's lying," and "They were looking out for him."

Next comes my three hours in the principal's office and a week's suspension.

SUDANESE KID
Gatouch Pan

I wasn't there when he left. I was at the Boys and Girls Club playing basketball after school. When I came back home, Jock and I were supposed to go to Open Gym to play basketball together. It was spring but still a little bit nippy outside.

When I walked in the door, I could tell my mom was upset about something. She was just sitting in the living room, staring, having blank thoughts. I asked, "What's wrong?" because I knew something was up. She took about a minute to respond, and then she turned and said, "Your brother took the next flight to Nebraska." When she said those words, her pupils were very small, but she wasn't crying. At the time she was wearing an African bright blue dress that my brother gave to her before he left. After she told me the news, I went to my room and dreamt about Jock and I playing basketball.

For the next six years, I only talked to him about three times on the phone. I missed him, everybody did. I didn't have anyone to play videogames with. I still had friends but no one like my brother. No one to talk to about some problems that I had. He always gave me the same speech–most of my problems are probably because I sometimes I speak my mind. If I don't like something, I'll speak. I'm not afraid to speak my mind, freedom of speech. But sometimes what's on your mind could be inappropriate or mean towards somebody else. He always told me, "If you have nothing good to say, don't say anything. Keep it all in your head, let it out when you're all alone."

My brother arrived from Nebraska on a cold Sunday night in February. When I first saw him come through the door, I knew it was him, not just because there were pictures all over the wall of him, but because I remembered him well enough. It felt like a newborn baby had just come because I hadn't seen him in six years. As I looked at him I felt like the luckiest kid in the world to have a brother like that. We shook hands. He said, "Yasalam! [oh my goodness, in Arabic!] You've changed!" He said I had grown taller and looked wiser.

Jock stayed with us for two weeks. After a couple of days, since I was gaming, he was wondering when I was going to do my homework. He asked me, "How is school?" I said, "It's fine." He checked my laptop and looked at my homework and documents to see if I had made progress over the years. He said, "Keep it up and you'll go somewhere." Having him back in the house made me feel like I could look up to somebody.

After the two weeks in Maine he had to leave. His wife and kids were missing him, and he had to go back to work. He was leaving again, but this time it wasn't as sad because I knew I was going to see him again soon. This summer I am going to visit him and his family in Nebraska.

Before he left, he gave me a necklace. It had the shape of Africa with African colors of yellow, red and green. In big, dark letters it said "Sudanese Kid." He said he got it from my grandma who lives in Sudan. I could tell it was from my grandma because it smelled like back home—like back at the farm, fruit everywhere. He got to see her in person recently, and he brought it back to give to me, to let me know she's still there and alive. Every time I look at the necklace it reminds me of his visit and of Africa and my family.

MY BROTHER RYAN
Kailyn Fitzgerald

We all had to get up at 3:00 am. It was hard for me to get out of bed, but I had to. This was the day we were taking my brother, Ryan, to the airport because he was going to basic training for the Air Force.

My mom, dad, my two brothers, sister, and I all got in the car. The car ride was quiet and awkward because no one knew what to say. The air in the car was damp with tears and cold air.

When we got to the airport, we didn't know where to go because we were all half asleep, but my dad knew because he works security there. At the gate everybody was so sad. My brother Brady wasn't sad because he going to be able to use Ryan's x-box when he was gone. My mom was taking pictures of everybody crying. I didn't understand why she was doing that. I was thinking that something bad could happen to Ryan and I would never see him again.

After we said our goodbyes and each of us had given him a hug and had said all we needed to say, there was a deep silence except for the announcements coming over the speakers and the sounds of airplane wheels hitting the pavement.

We were waiting for him to go. Fifteen minutes had passed by but nothing happened. Then suddenly we heard, "FLIGHT 436 TO SAN ANTONIO, TEXAS, AFB AIRFORCE BOARDING IN FIFTEEN MINUTES."

We each hugged him again and then we had to let him through security. We watched him in line with his friend, watched him take off his shoes and walk through the metal detector, and then turn to us and wave. We watched until we couldn't see him anymore. Then we went back to the car in the parking garage and drove home. I made pancakes for breakfast for all of us.

MY GRANDMOTHER
Maryama Abdi

My grandmother still lives in Somalia.
Sometimes I call her.
I love my grandmother. I was the closest person to her.
She used to take care of me. I was born
on our way to Kenya, at the border
when my mother went into labor with me.
But when we came to America,
there was no place for her here.
I wanted to stay with her but she said I had to go
with my mother,
that she was too old to take care of me.
She went back to Somalia.

You always believe in me, you always tell me,
"Don't let yourself down. No matter what."
You ask me how things are going,
I always say things are fine and going well.
But I never tell you the truth
of how things are really going with me.
I don't want to break your heart. Still you know
I am living a life that is not comfortable
without you in it.
I know you are far away but your love keeps me safe
and gives me peace.
And I wish you were here with me.
You would say, "Keep focused on your education,
Don't mess up your life."
You tell me, "I am waiting for you."
My dream is to build a mosque for you in Kismayo.

But I have to finish my education, and get a good job.

I have to have a plan,
I have to work hard, to achieve my goals.
We came to America for the opportunities
For the free education.
It will be arduous.
I am an immigrant, I am a Muslim, I am
A woman and I have dark skin. I am no fool.
I know it will be hard but
I will make my dream come true.
I will make your dreams come true, Grandmother.
My family knows how hard I have to work,
how hard it will be
To achieve my goals.
But they came to America so I could do this.

THE GUARDIAN
Randy German

My dad showed me two badges.
I was in his room upstairs.
The badges were on his uniform.
His uniform was light blue and the hat looked like
An upside down boat.
I think the uniform was cotton.
It was on a rack.

He took the uniform off the rack and showed me.
I saw two badges.
One of them was grey, blue, and red.

The other one looked like the front of an airplane.
You know those airplanes that have the propeller
Up front?
It was gold and grey.

They were both made of steel.

Dad was in the army
because he had nothing to do in the city,
So that is what he did.
He guarded three presidents
in the Dominican Republic.
He has a license plate of the limo
that the president rode in.
It has a gold color.
It is like a regular license plate
But it says "President of the Dominican Republic"
In Spanish.

"Presidente della Dominicana Republica."

And when he came to Maine he quit
But he kept the uniform and the training uniform.
He kept the badges and he had them in his closet
For two years. So when he took a vacation there
He could still train in case something bad happened.

I feel really, really proud of him,
I have the badges safe.

WHO I AM
Richard Akera

In my language, my name, Akera, means bravery. I was born in Uganda, a foreign land, and was raised there. Akera was my great grandfather's name, and he was a man who feared nothing in the world. My grandmother told me that when he was young, he always wanted to hunt with his father, but his father told him that he was too young. When he became a man, he started hunting with the villagers, and he became one of the great hunters. My name also means separation. My life so far is a story of separation, and one of courage.

When I was twelve, I heard from some people in the camp that if we went to America I would never be able to go back home. I have never been to my home, which is in Southern Sudan, a village called Pajok. Before he died, my dad went to the U.N. and asked for the forms for us to leave the country. We thought we were going to Australia at first, then they started interviewing us for the U.S. Every month, we would have to make the long walk, about three miles, to the office so they could interview us. It went on for years like that.

About four years after we started applying to leave, my grandma's visa came in. I never thought it would happen like that. I lost hope. I thought we would never leave, and they only wanted to take her. But then a year later, I had a crazy dream that we were in an airport with our bags, and then the weekend after the dream, a man called our house and told us that our names were on the board for a flight to the U.S. When she heard that, my mom started yelling God's name and jumping up and down. She said, "We are going to America!" We had a party with our family and friends.

When we were at the airport, my little brother saw a young white girl and he started crying and ran to me. He was scared because he wasn't used to white people. We heard the flight announced and we got on the plane. I was sweating and I felt like my heart was falling out—we had never been on a plane before. Eventually, we made it to Portland, where we all live with my grandma, together.

Through the pain and separation from my family and my homeland, sometimes I feel like giving up, like I want to quit. But there is something in my mind telling me: you started this, so finish it. Maybe it is that bravery that I inherited from my great grandfather, from those stories my grandmother told me. That courage comes from somewhere. No one should quit once you start something—be yourself and finish it. I will graduate from high school, and some day I will go back home for the first time.

2

PORTLAND, MAINE

THE DISAPPEARING CITY
Kordell Barcomb

The fort that has been untouched ever since the war is no longer the same silent prison it used to be. The underground chamber lay unnoticed for many years deep under the fort off the coast of Spring Point. Yes, it might look the same on the outside and maybe even a little on the inside but deep below the surface of the fort, even below the icy cold water of the North Atlantic, there lies a top secret bunker that is now home to a group of scientists that plan to do something that will shock not just the people of Portland, but also the world....

REPORT FROM THE JETPORT
Michee Runyambo

When we boarded our plane I sat in a window seat and put on my seatbelt. As we took off it felt like my stomach was glued to the ground below. It was both amazing and awful and I had never experienced anything like it. As we were in the air my uncle showed me a TV screen and told me that if I wanted to pick a movie I had to touch the screen. I had never seen a TV you touch to change channels, and that's when my uncle told me, "That's what's ahead, Michee."

A little while into the movie a lady came with some food and asked me what I wanted. I was kind of excited because it was the first time I was going to eat something that had not been prepared by the women in my family. The food was in a plastic box that listed the ingredients you were eating. I had some chicken, soup, and bread. The soup tasted nothing like my grandmother's, in fact it was awful. When we were flying above Ethiopia my uncle told me to look out the window. For as far as I could see there were clouds and I remembered how I always thought you could stand in the clouds. Far below me I saw the city of Nairobi. It was very beautiful. There were lights everywhere. I could see little houses and the streets were filled with what looked like hundreds of little toy cars. I wondered what America might look like from this height.

My uncle awoke me, asking, "Are you ready?" His smile told me we were close to our new home, and I was very exited when the plane touched down. When we landed my sister and I raced outside, because we had a deal that who ever put their feet on American ground last would have to carry the bags. I won, but my uncle made me carry them anyway, telling me, "That's not how a gentlemen acts." When we entered the airport in New York we had to separate as we passed through customs and immigration. I gave my papers to a serious looking lady who was very nice and said, "Thank you," a lot. She asked questions in English, some of which I didn't understand. I had taken English in Rwanda and hated it, but I would have to embrace the language to live in this country.

That evening we stayed in a beautiful hotel. The room we stayed in was the cleanest room I had ever been in. When morning came my uncle woke me up and we took a cab back to the airport. We got there at 6:45 and we got in our plane and it didn't take us more than hour to get to Maine, to Portland's jetport. When we got out I thought we were in Antarctica—it was so cold! I thought I wasn't wearing a jacket but I was wearing two of them!

In the jetport I saw my mom. I hadn't realized how much I missed her until I hugged her. All the pain of leaving my grandmother didn't feel as bad anymore. It took us about two hours to get home. On our way I saw a lot of trees and a moose. The moose was huge! It passed in front of the car that was in front of us and then it casually stopped in the middle of the street before it ran off. When we got home we celebrated with the rest of the family. I thought before I might feel out of place but I didn't. I felt like I was home.

A DAY IN THE CITY
Skyler Neal

A nearby restaurant makes a fuss with pots and pans filled with fresh smelly lobster while the seagulls squeak and squawk for the smallest tidbit of a hot dog or pretzel.

Shadows and sunlight make geometric shapes in the brick alleyway.

Cars whoosh past the slow moving sidewalks of a small park filled with trees, rocks, red bricks, and stone benches.

A white car rolls its wheels across the gray gravel, but suddenly stops, squeak! Soon after a yellow truck starts up its engine—varoom!

I walk into a kitchen store and as I stride past

row after row of vinegars, lunch boxes, bread spreads, and aprons the worn down old floor groans under the weight of my body. I brush my hand through aprons filled with colorful patterns and a small muted whoosh flows past my ears as layer after layer of aprons fall on top of swirly, curly, boxed shapes printed on the aprons.

STREET MUSICIAN
Libby George

There are very few things I feel every day. I feel the metal cross around my neck thump thump thumping on my chest as I take each grooving step, one with the music. I feel my clothes against my body, my headphones pulsing in my ears. I feel the gentle friction as my sandals drag along the roads, bricks, sidewalks of the city. I feel the dull vibrations of wrong notes in my throat. But what I feel the most are smiles, the smirks, the grins, the kids pretending to sing along. I love them. I bask in them. And I don't return the gazes. I keep on moving forward, as I've learned that's the method that breeds the reactions I want. It's all so very complex, the way people work, and I know I'll never come close to a breakthrough.

For years I was desperate, trying to understand the mind, the reactions of a human. I splurged what little money I had on a pair of headphones. I threw on my old Yankees hat, the ragged clothes I had. Then I sang. I sang in the midst of children, adults, babies. There were businessmen, the homeless, and musicians. I analyzed their reactions; the minute looks on their faces when they saw me. I tried singing louder, softer. I was a lonely man, too curious for his own good, trying to find wings out of nowhere.

What I did learn was this: there are no patterns in humankind. The only groupings that truly exist are those that are impossible for the human eye to see. Those that we do see will fall apart in the midst of anything unusual. I learned that one terrible person in a large crowd can infect those who are good with distrust and fear. But the most important lesson I learned is that there are those who smile and those who don't. At a passing stranger, at a puppy, at a cloudless sky, at nothing, at me. I don't see the frowns, they are invisible to me.

I don't hear many things every day. Mostly just the music and my voice; flat and soulless. Sometimes I hear a car horn, or a siren, but I try to block them out—they make me sad. I don't hear many voices. People don't like to break the barrier. They don't like to help me with my goal. I have it all planned out. Once my barrier is broken, once people are just beginning to realize I'm a person, I'll disappear. Vanish. No one knows my name. No one will notice when I show up one day in normal clothes, a silent tongue. I'll keep the cross. I would miss its thump thump thumping.

I don't hear a lot of things every day, so when I was approached today I removed my earplugs immediately. There were four of them, three girls—one older than the rest—and a boy. They wanted to take my picture with a strip of paper. It read, "Take flight." I smiled, but I did not return their camera's gaze. It was an amazing moment, their faces astonished by the normality of my voice, the way I work. It's what I live for, and I know they all learned priceless lessons.

It's later now. Dusk is settling in as the people are in their homes. Not me. I keep moving forward, flying forward, fueled by song and the knowledge that I've changed people.

THE BYSTANDER
Anna Mitchell

He wears a long jacket, plaid, silk and cashmere.
His shoes were polished by a maid at home,
now he wears them arrogantly.
His pants are black, along with a vintage belt
that he doesn't need to wear.
In his hand is a brief case, buckles of gold,
the rest, leather.
And his hat, made in Italy.
Custom designed to match the image on his cologne.

He wears a thread bare t-shirt, green.
It once read *Boston Celtics*.
He doesn't have shoes, only his feet to carry him.
He steps on his cigarettes;
his feet now a maze of burn scars.
Instead of shorts, the bathing suit he wears
is from the eighties, his father's retired one.
On his back is a pack:
One crumpled dollar
A soda bottle
A rope

That's all it holds.
His baseball cap is from a free pile,
moldy, old, dead.

IN TOMMY'S PARK
Eleanor McKibben

The man stands tall, his back straight, his feet planted firmly on the ground. A sturdy black case lies at the ready, magic slowly collecting inside. All around him, the city moves, people talking, walking, laughing, running to a bus, a date, a job. All of them not noticing. All of them obsessed with their own lives. Only the man stands still, as the people move around him like a river over a smooth rock.

The case is clicked open. Heads turned, some anticipating the event, some startled or curious. Most passerby looked straight ahead, however, focused on their goals, their plans, their intentions. The musician played a few short chords. Some people paused, in mid-sentence, mid-purchase, or mid-cell phone conversation. Heads turned on their shoulders.

Only when the guitarist started to play a second did they fully stop and share, transfixed by the music. And just for a moment, everyone had the same feelings, the same thoughts, the same intentions. The song flew through the city air, familiar yet different to everyone.

The music stopped. The moment ended. Everyone started to disperse. After all, they had things to do. Places to go. People to meet. Onward they walked, already forgetting the moment they were united, listening to music.

ARBORETUM
Eva Griffiths

It was tall, beautiful, and brilliant as a city tree. Not a country tree. It was branched out wide. It splayed out, trying to shade those who were sweltering. It was encased in cement. It was suffocated, yet it lived. It was an imprisoned body, but in spirit it was free. Nobody realized how important the tree was. They would ask for shade and it willingly gave it. They would ask for shelter and it would try to rearrange its leaves, even if it meant getting more wet herself. For those who asked for comfort, she would let them lean their back on her as they sullenly smoked silently in the night, the only color was the orange glow of the cigarette. Every day she would straighten herself and try her best to touch a cloud, to become tall and receive more sunlight. She never got to.

It was a cloudy, dreary day when the truck pulled up beside her, carrying a man with a yellow hardhat and a neon yellow-and-orange vest on. He slammed the door shut and sloshed through the muck puddle that had splashed her a million times before to the back of the truck where he pulled out a large orange case, which, to her horror, contained a chainsaw.

The beloved tree rustled to her neighbor, "I think I am done, take care of the people for me." The man with the yellow hardhat started toward the tree as she thought that she could maybe, possibly, touch the clouds. She couldn't. Not in 10, 9, 8, 7, 6, 5, 4, 3, 2, - she thought of the man who always leaned against her and smoked at ten o'clock, every night. She thought of the mother and baby who once dashed under her for rain protection. How would she protect anyone as a stump? Where would the man smoke every night at ten o'clock? Not here. A stump was nothing, merely a thing that eventually rots away.

The beautiful tree braced herself for the pain, the grinding away at her torso that she was sure she could not survive. "I am an elderly tree," she rustled. "I would have died soon anyway." The saw slashed her side as she weakened her branches. Her top that had held her lush leaves and branches had been violently thrown to the ground. The tree was being chopped, piece-by-piece, until she was a stump. Merely a stump. She couldn't shade. She couldn't protect. She couldn't comfort.

She sat there feeling forgotten as people tossed cigarettes in her patch of grimy dirt and ashes. They walked past her as if nothing was ever there. The once loved tree was still there, trying. Trying to touch a cloud.

ARABICA
Hannah Van Alstine

Freshly brewed coffee beans and pastries
just out of the oven
Make up the inspiring scent.
Tap
Tap
Tap.
Busy fingers against laptop keys.
"Brrrrrring" of the cash register.

The quiet, brilliant speak of writers chatting,
The flip and crinkle of books being
devoured by eager readers
And the rustle of newspaper pages
Are the sounds that swirl in the
Thick and aroma-filled air.

Large, framed oil paintings hang
on the ancient brick walls
Featuring lopsided eggplants,
And a trio of fat, juicy pears.
Oddly shaped lights that can't be classified
As any particular shape, hang above the pay counter,
Which is littered with warped flower vases,
Home to many species of flowers.

Bikes in various colors are lined artistically outside
On the old sidewalk.
A wooden bench with wobbly wood
and rusting metal armrests is
Propped up on the tall brick walls of the building.
A man is perched on the bench,
Half chatting with passersby,
Half working on his almost
completed crossword.

The door creaks obnoxiously as it swings
Open and close,
Open and close,
As people enter and leave the inspirational
Arabica Café.

44

COMMERCIAL STREET COBBLESTONE
Lucy Kilbreth

The one cobblestone stands alone,
Not noticed by anyone or anything.
It is the only pink granite stone on the street.

Imagine its story…

Long forgotten over eons,
Run over for so long by cars,
Trampled by countless shoes,
Where are its brethren?

Imagine the carriages and hooves it has seen
And the stories it has to tell.

OCCUPANTS OF WIDGERY WHARF
Alyssa Donovan

The shallow water underneath this wharf
Nudges the hulls, the rocks, the sand
And recounts to them all a tasteless joke
That starts his rippling laughter.
The hulls, the rocks; they are quiet,
Shrugging off the advance of the waves.
The hulls rock and stare at their reflections,

Twisted by many undulating folds. The rocks
Dare not to abandon their scenic perch, but the sand
Is swayed away by the trivial antics of the sea
And decides to forget her humorless neighbors.
All is now calm with the swift departure
Of the bothersome sea and the sand,
And the wharf is graced again
With its original brand of beauty.

PORTLAND THROUGH MY EYES

Emmanuel Muya

When I was little, before I moved to the US from Congo, I had plenty of myth in my mind. I thought that the US was full of skyscrapers and everywhere was clean and shiny. I used to watch movies that were made in the USA and they always showed these pretty and busy places, like New York City and California. I was so fascinated by the beautiful sights in the movies, and sometimes, during my sleep, I was dreaming about them.

Since we were kids, my friends and I always talked about life in the USA. Most of the time we used to make up stories, and sometimes we would exaggerate—for instance, I used to daydream about flying cars. Sometimes we would think about how we'd go to the US, if someday we got a chance.

Miraculously, my family finally did get that chance—my dreams were going to come true. The first day I landed in Atlanta I immediately knew I was in the USA because the airport was so huge and sophisticated. I saw people driving fancy cars just like I saw in the movies. All the roads were wide and paved on the way to where we were heading. There was a lot of diversity—people of all races.

After a few months, we had to move from Atlanta to Maine. On the airplane, when we flew over Portland, my eyes were looking down at the view and my first perspective was: Maine is like a USA village—but not the type of village I knew. Portland was different and looked a little old. I think it's because it was winter, when the dirt gets mixed up with the snow and everything is kind of grimy. Also, the roads were tiny. Most of the houses were small compared to those in Atlanta. But I saw that Maine was nothing like the USA I had dreamt and heard of.

I asked my mom, "How long will we have to stay here?" I know my parents felt the same way I did. But she told me we would settle here, integrate, and learn to understand the system. When we landed, some friend came and drove us to their house. On our way, my eyes were looking all over the place and I saw many homeless people in the street. That shocked me. And the town was very small. I felt desperate and I thought I wasn't in the USA. But I had no choice but to let things take care of themselves.

As I integrated into the community—playing soccer, meeting other people from Congo, making friends at school, being part of The Telling Room—my perspective started to change. I realized that every place is different and has its own infrastructure. People in

Maine may not feel the same way as other people. Their accents are different. I've learned that every state may not live up to my myth, and I'm okay with that.

3

EATING AND
DRINKING

THE DOGFISH CAFE
Carter Williams

It was late fall and nobody had woken up yet. I tended to sleep in on Saturdays, but was unable to on this occasion. I watched TV for hours while waiting for my parents to get up and make me breakfast. Some weekends my dad would take me to the Dogfish Café down the street for one of their gourmet breakfast sandwiches, which is what I was craving this day.

Finally, I couldn't stand it any longer and I marched up to my parents' bedroom. Living downtown, I had a pretty sheltered childhood, and although I was about ten years old at the time, I had never much walked anywhere on my own.

After explaining my starving situation to my parents, they handed me money to go the Dogfish Cafe, as though I had done it a million times. I accepted the money, surprised by their trust, and left the house. I exited our driveway, not know what to expect on this morning all by myself. Next, I walked past the house of our neighbor Fred, who was above me, busy roofing. Rounding the corner, I spotted the "Witch Lady" who had stolen my father's bike and some of our lawn furniture a few years back, and crossed the street to avoid her.

After another minute of power walking in fear, I arrived at the Dogfish and ordered my breakfast. I felt very grown up sitting at the counter in my big Carhartt jacket with no escort.

BAKLAVA IN THE BUGATTI

Jennifer Benjamin

If I had a car it'd be a Bugatti. I would drive it fast. I'd listen to hip-hop music like Tyga, Lil' Wayne, or Wu Tang. My car would smell fresh and clean. It'd be nice and expensive. One rule I would have about my car is that NO EATING would be allowed inside it. I hate messes in cars—especially when there are a bunch of food crumbs on the seats. This reminds me of the dirtiest car I've ever been in.

Three years ago I got into the grossest car I've ever seen. It was my friend Randy's Kia. It was a silver car. He had to put duct tape all over the front and back of the car to hold it together—silver duct tape to match the silver paint. There were bottles and trash all over the floor. The cup holders were sticky. The seats had burns all over them from a lighter. On the back of the front seat someone had written "faggot" and then drew an arrow pointing to where Randy sat. When you sat in the car it smells like you were sitting in a dumpster.

I decided I would never let anyone eat in my car or do gross stuff in my car. Not just because it grossed me out but I knew it would disgust anyone who got into my car, too, and I don't want that. My mom won't let me get my driver's license because she doesn't trust me, but if she did I can only imagine what it'd be like if someone asked to get in my car with food.

Imagine this:

After school one day Nicky comes up to my car.

"Yo, give me a ride!" she says. She is carrying a Subway sandwich, a pickle and a .99 cent blue Big Gulp. This is what is in the sandwich:

Turkey
Ham
Roast Beef
Provolone
Pepper Jack
Spinach
Banana Peppers
Oil
Mayo
Mustard

It's a footlong. I look at her and know for a fact that she'll spill the Big Gulp all over my car and that the second she takes a bite of the sandwich it'll fall apart cause it's so big. I am shocked she even asks me.

"No, you're going to spill that," I say. I lock my doors and drive away.

As I drive away she gives me a death stare. Her eyes get very small; her mouth opens but I can't hear her yelling 'cause my music is bumpin'.

No one, not even friends, can eat in my car.

No lasagna in the Lamborghini
No beans in the Beemer
No meatballs in the Mercedes Benz
No baklava in the Bugatti
No mustard in the Mustang

SNACK SHACK FRIES
Michael Feely

Eating my salty fries at Crescent Beach's Snack Shack, my friend and I see a patrol of seagulls on the shack's roof. One is looking to the left, one is looking to the right, and five are looking to the front—for food left out or forgotten.

I smell my fries and so do the seagulls. One seagull says, "Hey, come over here. This kid's got fries!"

Now the one from the left glides over to the front, making six on the front, which is scarier. Their white feathers gleam in the blue sky. I can feel the greasy fries and I know that the seagulls soon will too.

I go inside to help my friend find the trash, but then I hear all the seagulls yelping to get my fries! I sprint over to my fries and I yelp too. My ketchup is spilled all over my fries, so I know I have to get messy.

As I finish up my fries, I hear an astonishing scream. A seagull zooms by this guy's head, targeting his junk food trash.

"Whoa! Did you just see that seagull?" I thought about how scared I would be if I were that guy.

I figure that before that seagull's flight, its captain of patrol said, "Hey Sergeant! I need you to go risk your life to go past that guy's head and try to snatch his tasty looking trash. That's an order. Fly for the fries!"

Well, I guess that the captain's order didn't work.

While we walk back to our picnic blanket on the beach, we see a sorrowful one-legged seagull next to the lifeguard stand. We know that he is not part of the patrol. Or is he?

HOT POT WITH BUTTER
Jessica Thear

Every time I cook meat it burns because I enjoy my food crispy. The hot butter along with the beef sear my taste buds. It's amazing that two simple ingredients can create such an impact on my cravings. The taste of butter also brings back memories of my late uncle Thân.

I eat Thai hot pot at my grandparents' house. I eat it along with my grandpa who was drinking Hennessy. My grandmother is also present and she is enjoying her Jagermeister. All thirteen of my cousins are there. My father and his four other siblings are there. I also know my uncle is there in spirit.

The house is crammed. No walking space. There is a huge griddle with the food cooking on it. Everyone has his or her own dish. Couches are moved in order to have space to eat. The room is loud. The room smells like melted candles and incense. The incense is part of my family's offering to my uncle in the other world. This was his favorite dish as well.

Grandpa has one arm. He is a man with a lot of heart. Something that proves this would be when the king of Cambodia came to the village that my grandparents resided in, and the way he acted when the king requested that my grandmother become one of his mistresses. My grandfather got on his knees and begged him not to take his wife. He was willing to give everything he had including his gold and livestock. And even his own life.

FARMER'S MARKET
Hannah Grant

Beautiful, bursts of blackberries
Bright, boastful beets
Blue bites of blueberries
Bashful, bumbling broccoli

Crisp, crunchy cucumbers
Cheerful, charming cherries
Gloating, gossiping green beans

Positively puny peas
Plump, peaceful potatoes
Ripe, red raspberries

Sharp, saucy scallions
Tasty, tough turnips
Toppling, tarnished tomatoes

Fresh, flavorful fruits fiddle for farmer's markets.

DOUGHNUTS AND ELEVATION BURGER
Jean Claude Zarate

I woke up and looked out the car window, and it seemed like the sky was mourning, crying for me. As we entered Maine I remembered some of the stuff I had left behind. We left my sister's turtle at my aunt's. We separated the turtle from its friends who it would probably never see again. We left our beautiful two-story house alone, empty with no one to comfort. We left my mom's side of the family, we left my cousins, we left our friends to find Maine.

I rolled down my window and the blowing wind took most of the strong smell of the trees, but I could still smell them. As I bit into a doughnut it reminded me of the doughnut shop back home at the mall in Lima. Their doughnuts were baked fresh daily and you could watch them make the dough. As I bit it I didn't yet know about the difference between real doughnuts with fresh frosting and cheap chemically made frosting.

Our family welcomed us with warm hugs. The next day my uncle took us to various places. He took us to Portland Head Light and other places. I remember going to the mall, thinking it was so BIG but now it's really small for me. I remember trying Panda Express hating it and throwing it away. Now I love Panda Express, and I guess my taste for food changed.

There is a McDonalds in the food court at the mall. The McDonalds in Peru was in the middle of Lima. It was at least six stories high and very wide like a hotel. We never went in there because I was afraid of Ronald McDonald. Sometimes my cousins went there and the Happy Meals were in a box like in the commercials and not in a paper bag like here.

Now Maine feels natural. School isn't confusing. I'm learning a third language and doing better than ever. And now and then my aunt sends me a picture of my sister's pet turtle, which is now huge. School lunch is still kinda disgusting, and many people if not everyone agrees with me. I have gotten used to chemically made stuff, but our family doesn't go to any fast food place other than Elevation Burger, which is 100% organic.

SUMMER SAUSAGES
Lucy Kilbreth

Sausages sizzle on the sidewalk in summer,
With salt in the sun
And they are sloppy and simple.
They are simply salty,
Sizzled and scrambled.
They're good with snakes.
They are also sandy.

TEA FOR ME
Aden Issack

It was raining. I walked from school to my house, which was not a long way. I lived on the second floor and had to climb many stairs to get to my family's apartment in Portland, Maine. I was thirteen years old. I opened the door and it was quiet in the house. I usually would hear my little brothers yelling.

"Hello," I said. But nobody was there. I checked the rooms and nobody was there. I put my bag down and went into the kitchen to look for some food. I opened the refrigerator and found an apple and ate that but I was still hungry because I hadn't eaten lunch at school. I didn't like the food at school that day. I tried to make some pasta but I was scared because of the fire. I had never cooked for myself before. I called my mom on her cell phone but she didn't answer. She was usually home.

This was the first time I'd been alone in a place where I lived—in Jilib, Kesmayo, Mogadishu, Virginia, or Portland. I wasn't sure what to do. I heard really loud music coming from someone else's apartment upstairs. I tried to ignore it but I couldn't. I was so hungry and couldn't find any food that I knew how to make.

Then I decided that I would try to make tea for the first time in the United States. I took the kettle and put some water into it then put it on the stove. The water boiled and so much steam came out when it was ready. After the water boiled and was very, very hot I poured it into a small glass cup. I thought that this was tea. I never thought that maybe I'd have to add anything else to it. I'd never made it on my own. My mother had made it when I was growing up in Jilib, or my Uncle when we moved to Mogadishu during the war, but not me.

I remembered my mom saying that she added sugar to tea to make it sweeter, so I took the Hannaford sugar box off of the shelf and poured it into the cup. I wanted to take a sip right away but it was too hot so I put it in the freezer. When I finally took a sip it tasted like something else—it wasn't tea. I threw the cup into the sink and gave up. I went into the living room and started watching TV. That was the last time I had tea.

I will never drink it again until I can go back to my country of Somalia and have the dark familiar tea with its fresh goat milk. That is the only tea to me.

PANCAKES FOR BREAKFAST
Gaby Baez

The sun was so bright it shined through the curtains. The room was quiet but you could hear the little birds tweeting from the outside. I opened the curtains and woke up my friend Ashley. We were kind of hungry so we got up, brushed our teeth and we went downstairs to find something to eat.

When Ashley went to open the refrigerator door she found a little note on the door from her mom and it said, "Dear Girls, I went out to buy some things. I won't be back for a while. Pancakes are in the cabinets if you ladies want any. See you soon. From Mom."

Since no one was in the house we decided to put some music on to dance to. We put on On The Floor by Jennifer Lopez. Then we went on to look for the bag of pancakes. We looked everywhere until we finally found them. We opened the fridge and took out the milk and eggs and started mixing the pancake mix. We poured the flour into a basket. Ashley poured the milk and I cracked the eggs. The batch got harder and harder to mix because it was thickening. After mixing the pancake mix we poured it on a little pan to cook them.

While they were cooking we decided to step outside for some fresh air. It was so warm out, the sun was super bright, it was our first week of summer vacation and summer was actually here; the only good thing about Maine. We said we would sit down and get a quick two-minute tan but it was so quiet and peaceful that we forgot about the time.

Out of nowhere we heard a loud alarm beeping! We freaked out and ran into the house. It was a pancakes disaster! There was smoke everywhere and we got kind of scared. We opened all the windows and brought the pancakes outside. The alarm stopped beeping and we calmed down.

We picked up the mess we made and started a new batch but this time we watched them very carefully. When they were done we sat at the table and ate our pancakes with bacon, and when we were done eating we continued with our sun tanning. A while later, Ashley's mom came home and she asked us, "How was your morning, girls? What have you done?" We answered her with laughter.

SWEETIE SOUP
Amy Tran

The soup is sweet and spicy
and bright orange and red.
We call the soup "Sweetie."
The soup is like nothing I have eaten before.
It tastes like it has a lot of garlic in it.
I am at home eating with my mom, dad and brother.

Mom is wearing a blue tee shirt and blue jeans,
Dad is wearing navy blue shorts and a green t-shirt.
My brother is wearing blue jeans and a blue tee.

We all look out the window next to our glass circular table
and we watch the sunset. It is orange and red,
the sky above it is blue, purple, orange and red.
Suddenly the room is quiet.
Everybody is shocked by the prettiness of the sunset,
sitting perfectly still, like statues.
My mother has her spoon halfway to her mouth
and her lips are apart but she doesn't move.
The yellow wall behind us turns the color of the sky.
The soup and my family's faces have a similar orange glow.
We watch the sun sink and suddenly I remember
a story my grandmother told me about eating pho
by the ocean,
watching the end of a day.

My family was in Ho Chi Min city in Vietnam
listening to the noises of the cars and motor scooters
whizzing past.
Their soup was sweet and salty and very spicy
and they all slurped the noodles making their lips tingle.
When the sunset is over we go back to the soup.
The soup is so creamy.
The flavor explodes in my mouth.
I keep hearing the spoons clinking on the bowl
and the slurping of my mom, dad, and brother
eating the soup.

POT ROASTS AND KOOL-AID STANDS
Laura Holt

My real Maine is countless twelve-ounce coffee cups
in the backseat of my mother's station wagon.
It's cheap cars, but mostly trucks on our dirt and
tarred, potholed roads.
It's me at fifteen driving down the back roads
and my sister screaming, "Brakes, hit the brakes!"
It's every kindergartener learning how
to plant a tree in the schoolyard.
It's diner food, pot roasts, and Kool-Aid stands.

Maine is the place with sweet elder neighbors
with kind hearts and antique teakettles.
It's seeing your friend's parent can
their garden-grown tomatoes in holey jeans
and a stained white t-shirt that has UPTA camp
printed on the front.
It's pointless trips to Wal-Mart
in thirty-five degree weather
just to get a thing or two.
It's standing by the window in a dimly lit room
feeling the sunlight.

Maine is walking past houses and seeing smoke flow
from old chimneys.

Real Maine is close and distant but strong.
Real Maine is pure and sweet maple syrup
over Sunday morning pancakes.
Real Maine is having your own ice skating rink
in your backyard.
It's a place where you wander into the woods
and taste, look, and listen.

4

ENTERTAINMENT

SEARCH FOR FUN
Ali Aljubyly

I lived in Iraq, in Karbala. I loved my family, but the most important thing to me was just to have fun. I felt like nothing could hold me back.

My dad was in the States. He had been there for ten years working to get us a better life. Then he came back to Iraq to take our family to Jordan. We stayed in Amman, getting our documents together so we could join him in the U. S. My dad, whose name is Kadhum, is a man who had a hard life; nothing good happened to him. Whenever he tried to do good for his family, it never seemed to go his way.

After a year in Amman, we left for the States. It was the longest ride of my life. As soon as we got off the plane in Chicago, we saw my dad. I remember he gave me ten dollars. When my dad gave me the money, it meant the world to me. I remember holding the ten-dollar bill in my hand and it made me feel like my dad and I were rich!

I didn't realize how much more valuable it was in Iraq than it was in the States, but I believed I could do anything and get whatever I wanted with that ten-dollar bill. I've always been a curious person, someone who tries to understand the unexplainable, for instance, the Bermuda Triangle. After a few years in the United States I had become somewhat of an American. Whenever a new game system came out, I wanted to have it. I felt obligated to have whatever kids in my school had.

When I was in Iraq, I could provide for myself. If

I wanted to buy something, I'd find some copper from an old car or some machine, sell it, and have the money I needed. My friends and I made up our own games, like "sand in the bottle." A bunch of kids would fill a bottle with sand and make a ball out of socks. One of us would knock the bottle over with the sock ball and everyone would run. Everyone understood how the game was played. Every year, in "kite season," kids would buy a kite or make one. I made mine. We were very competitive. Each of us would get a special string: it was sharp and would cut the string of another kite. There was a system: if you cut another kite, you would sell it to the owner or to someone else, or you'd keep it.

After I'd been here for a while, my creative spirit began to fade. In Iraq, I had this leadership quality: I'd make up a game and pretty soon, everyone would be playing it. When I came to the States, that changed. Whenever I suggested an activity, kids would say no, they wanted to play video games or watch TV or get on the computer. This was new to me so I felt like I had to explore the way they played, and eventually I lost interest in my way of playing. I became lazy and sat around watching TV, playing video games and using the computer like everyone else.

Whenever I finished a game, I'd get a new one. Soon I wanted the new more expensive games and I didn't have enough money. I asked my dad for more money, and he told me he had to pay the bills with the money he made. He suggested that I get a job so I could buy what I wanted. It wasn't that easy. I was young and not qualified to get a job. I began to realize that I wasn't rich. My idea that anyone who comes to the US would become rich instantly was a myth. Still, I believe that if I try hard enough, I can achieve my dreams, and I might even have fun doing it, too.

VISIT A PLAYGROUND
Isabelle Murray

I slip my shoes off and take my first step onto the playground, bursting with imagination and wonder. This place is a land of mystery, where nobody knows what comes next, and everybody forgets what came before. I approach the swings, but I don't know if I really want to be here. I am nervous, nervous about what will happen if I jump on that swing. Will I fly off? No, I won't. I plop myself onto the seat and take my first leap. Pushing myself off of the side bar with all my might, I soar through the air. I feel like a bird, zipping through the wind.

The smooth plastic glides steadily across my skin. The swing moans on its rusty hinges as it sways to a steady pace: 1,2,3…1,2,3. I look up from my book and the wind blows in my face. It is a calm breeze, though. As I rock back and fourth it reminds me of when I was a kid, lying in my mother's lap, her warm arms around me, her hair spilling over my face. I lay my head down on her trusty legs, with the hope that she will read me another one of her stories. But those days are gone, I have matured and even though I am still her little angel, I will never again be that small. For now, I don't have to worry about anything. My imagination can run wild, I can be anything on this big blue swing.

LISTEN TO MUSIC
Chrispo Niyokwizerwa

My name is Chrispo Niyokwizerwa. I was born in Rwanda in 1993. And this is me, with my talent, sending a message about how music changes your life.

I grew up listening to music, and at the age of nine, music started influencing me. I knew it was my talent, but I made an early mistake. By the age of eleven I was surrounded by a lot of talented singers. I knew this guy who worked at the music company in my country. His name was Mandela, and he was a huge, light skinned guy. He was one of the people I knew who made good music at that time. When I asked him if I could be in the music company, he exploded laughing at me. He said that I was too young to think about it. He was right, I was really young.

Giving up on music was like breaking up with a girl. Though I stopped thinking about music as much as I used to, I didn't forget about it. I kept thinking about how I was going to pay for recording but I never had the opportunity. As days went on I slowly lost my music skills.

In my second year at Portland High School I joined The Telling Room. I was excited about the great opportunity I was going to receive to become a leader and a great writer. The Telling Room was not only about education, but it also changed my life. I met Sonya Tomlinson who was going to be our songwriting teacher. Her first introduction was a rap freestyle. I looked and my eyes opened wide. It was amazing to see a woman rap because in my country women sing but they don't rap.

I didn't know where I was going to start again with music. I took the CD that had a beat recorded on it and put it in the computer. My headphones were already in my ears. I listened to the beat for some time but I couldn't get the idea back. It was like my mind was searching for where the music had gone.

I went back to try one more time. I laid on my bed looking up words and I closed my eyes slowly as the song started. My body felt so cold as I listened to the beat. It was like a legend was rising again. My memory flashed back to music and I opened my eyes. The words started playing in my mind as I wrote them on the paper. I started spitting verses like I was hyper from eating a lot of sugar. My body felt light and weak but my head felt heavy.

ATTEND A SUMMER BEACH PARTY
Otra Patel

One day I was with my aunt and uncle and we were at a summer party at a beach. It was in Maine near Brunswick, and it was very warm and really windy. I could feel the cold breeze on my face and arms because I had a short sleeve shirt on and forgot my jacket in the car. We went toward the area where the party was and my aunt and uncle were setting tables up while my sister Urja and I were looking around. I could smell the sea.

We asked to go to the beach because it was boring

being near the adults talk, and I felt like something was wrong but there wasn't anything I forgot or didn't realize.

We sat on the bench near the cool windy breeze. We felt very good in the open wide warm air smelling the amazing ocean. I told my sister that we were in a very calm place. I asked my aunt if we could go look and touch the water. She said yes so we walked along the shore and my sister started making weird sand castles and I started laughing because they fell apart. I could feel the warm sun in my face.

When it was time to eat we had corn and potatoes on the grill stuffed with spices and hot chilies. It was really good but really hot. I couldn't finish my whole plate but I did finish the corn. My aunt called us over to help out putting the stuff away while the people they knew played cricket.

Suddenly, it started to get dark so my aunt and uncle were cleaning up the mess that they made. I was getting bored so I looked around and fell to the ground and just stayed there looking at the clouds and thought of how summer in Maine is beautiful and it's pretty much the only good and nice thing about Maine.

It was time to go so I grabbed my jacket and headed to the car. It started to rain so everyone walked fast trying to get into their cars and I saw my uncle run as fast as he could toward our car, which was really funny and made me laugh like there was no tomorrow. Our car was all wet and when cold air came I started drawing on the windows. I love doing that—it's funny and cool.

APPROACH A HAUNTED HOUSE

Meghan Kelly

I don't really recall when I first became convinced that the house was haunted. There weren't any of the signs that traditionally indicated such a house: no drab, peeling paint or broken windows or creaking porches. But it stood empty constantly, and this was what finally persuaded me that it was haunted when I was younger. Otherwise, why wouldn't the occupants ever be there?

I knew that there were occupants; my dad had told me so when I'd asked, saying that they traveled frequently, which was why they were never there. I thought this was a rather weak, even evasive answer. Even if the owners of the house traveled, they had to come home sometime, I was sure. And this house would be such a perfect place to return to: it was the biggest on the street, with a soaring roof and beautiful round windows. There was no explanation for this constant absence, I reasoned with youthful logic, unless they were avoiding their house's ghosts. I was determined to find out more.

Luckily for my curiosity, the annual neighborhood potluck was fast approaching. Like every year, it would be at Luigi's house, which was an ideal place from which to conduct an investigation that my parents would certainly have frowned upon, had they known of it. The small gap between the hedge at the back of Luigi's patio and his next-door neighbor's fence would provide the perfect, undetectable escape route.

At the party, I gathered together the other neighborhood kids in the cul-de-sac, away from our parents' notice. My younger brother, two bickering brothers from down the street, and another boy who showed surprisingly little disdain for my theory about the house despite being a year or two my senior all listened as I told them of my plan. All four quickly agreed.

We returned to the party and acted as usual—which meant chasing each other around the street and darting back to the food tables to grab cookies our mothers wouldn't have wanted us eating—so as no to attract attention. The moment we'd judged we could slip away safely, we quickly disappeared into the tunnel, with me in the lead.

It was hot inside, hotter even than in the full sunshine, and the air was close and heavy and hard to breathe. Hordes of mosquitoes dwelt inside the space, and were thrilled to welcome us there by swarming in thickly oppressive clouds. We raced along the passageway, hearts pounding with the knowledge of adventure and excitement and risk.

One by one, we emerged into the open, covered with itching welts but grinning triumphantly. We congregated briefly on the sidewalk and looked at the front of the house, which was strangely sinister even in the bright sunshine. Although I could not qualify what gave the building its eerie feel, I know everyone else perceived it too, because we all moved a little closer together. Then we crept stealthily across the street and into the backyard of the haunted house.

We explored the yard cautiously, on the lookout for any sign of ghosts. Finally I worked up the courage to look in one window, which was draped promisingly with tendrils of cobwebs. As I stood on tiptoe to peer over the windowsill, a branch suddenly broke off a tree behind us with a thunderous crack and plummeted to the ground.

We all jumped. Then at once we dashed back across the street and through the tunnel, bursting out of it at the party again, where luckily our brief disappearance had gone unnoticed.

The experience had left us all gleefully terrified. Throughout the whole rest of the party, I was on edge; I startled easily and frequently glanced over my shoulder, as if expecting something to materialize behind me whenever I wasn't looking. Though we had admittedly found no concrete evidence of a ghostly presence at the house, I at least remained not one bit less convinced that it was there.

PLAY HOOPS
Colby Martin Hogan

Finally I am at the hoop. I dare myself to make a basket without looking. I turn backward somewhere around the foul line and close my eyes. My veins are tingling and I have butterflies in my stomach. I can't stop thinking how cool it will be to make that impossible shot without looking. I even find myself betting five dollars with my brother that I will make it. I try to relax by taking a deep breath. I close my eyes and picture the perfect shot in my head.

I'm standing to the side at a distance and can see the hoop and me in profile. The blue ball leaves my hands in slow motion and rotates as it rolls off my fingertips. The ball goes up and up against the blue sky in a perfect arc, passing in front of clouds and then comes down through the hoop. "Swish." The sound is perfect, light and smooth like a wave crashing onto the beach.

I exhale.

Now I believe in myself, so I go and take the shot. It's smooth and fast leaving my hands and I can see houses and trees and the backboard, and the ball is spinning. It dives through the net like the kids diving at the rec center pool.

I throw one fist in the air and whisper, "Yes." I turn to my brother, who isn't really there, and hold out my hand for the five bucks.

GET A TAN
Polina Beloglazova

I was with a friend, Sophia. We'd only known each other for a short time, less than year. She is taller than I am and she runs pretty fast. Her eyes and hair are brown.

When our parents didn't want to drive us to Old Orchard Beach, we went by ourselves, on foot. It was a hot day and not many cars were on the road. We were walking barefoot and I was holding my shoes in my hands. There weren't many rocks on the road and there was grass and woods on either side. The walk was so long that we stopped four times to look at nature. For the first forty minutes, we were talking about our parents, about how mean they are. I was giving her advice, and we were speaking in Russian.

After a while I turned my head and I saw the sun going down. We talked for a while about going back because it was getting dark. When I suggested that, Sophia said, "It's only a short way more." We kept walking, but within twenty minutes the sky turned to purple and darker blue and I could see the stars.

GO ON A CAMP ADVENTURE
Abby Dwelley

My dad calls to tell me that I am going to camp with my cousins. I pack clothes and goggles and of course a bathing suit, because when we are at camp we don't take our bathing suits off all day. Six of us pile in the truck, and we settle in with some music and games to pass the time.

The camp is on Sebec Lake. Whenever I tell people where I am going they always think I say Sebago Lake, which is a very popular summer destination in Maine. But this is much farther north. It takes three hours to get there.

The driveway alone is a five-minute trip. When you turn onto it, you feel the bumps on the dirt road and know you are close. As the car kicks up gravel, it sounds like maracas shaking. At the end are my dad's and my uncle's camp with a house and a cabin. They are both made of unpainted wood so they look like they belong with the tall trees surrounding them. They are right on the water.

As soon as we arrive, we run to the dock and jump into the lake in our clothes because we are too excited to change. Immediately the chill hits me. I am wearing my dad's t-shirt to stay comfy during the drive, and once that gets soaked it feels even bigger and heavier like the water is a weight. I pull it away from me and the air fills it up and I am light like a balloon. We slide our goggles down over our eyes and explore underwater. I find a rock and lift it up releasing a burst of tiny fish, too many to count, that swim away like a silent explosion.

After swimming, we jump on a giant trampoline. We bounce so high it feels like we can touch the clouds. When we get cold, we eat gooey s'mores by the fire. Then when it's time to go to bed we hop into the two sets of bunk beds and go to sleep.

We wake up to the sound of bacon sizzling. We eat a gourmet meal of scrambled eggs, and sausage and toast and orange juice. Then we shoot some pool and go swimming all day long. Same thing all over again, but we never get sick of it. We love it at camp.

READ A BOOK
Oona MacKinnon-Hoban

The musty smell of books was the first thing Elena could truly smell in the morning. It awakened her senses better than any coffee could. This fact was only true because every morning at 8:00 am sharp Elena arrived at the Abraham Memorial Library to begin her job there.

Yes, Elena was a librarian. No, not the dowdy tweed and lipstick wearing kind. She was just a girl with a great need for money and an even greater love for books. Despite the fact that her friends deemed her line of work "socially unacceptable," Elena loved it.

She would arrive right on time every morning, work at the counter for a while, organize the books, wander around the vast library, read to the kids and then at 5:00 pm head home. It was simple, but it was enough for her.

When she was in the library, she felt safe. Untouchable almost. True, she wasn't the most social person and only on a rare occasion would a boy give her a second glance. But in the library, surrounded by countless books, Elena was the queen. And no one could knock her off her throne.

ENJOY A DR. PEPPER MOMENT
Nicole Griffin

What is joy?
Joy is when fizzy soda is opened at my toes and
The bubbles flurry up to my soul.

What is sorrow?
Sorrow is when the sun slowly disappears and
Does not want to show again.

What is pride?
Pride is when my neck stretches out and
I can see above the clouds.
What is excitement?
Excitement is when lightning strikes me and
I can no longer control my body.

What is anger?
Anger is a lion locked in a cage all day and
He's just roaring to get out.

What is antsy?
Antsy is when I walk outside during a windy day and
My hair can't figure out
If it wants to be in my face or on my shoulders.

TOUR A COLLEGE CAMPUS
Ralph Houanche

I'm controlling the soccer ball with my right foot, running toward the opposite team's net. My fans are screaming my name and I can't disappoint them. I have to score a goal because my team is down one-nothing. I'm one on one with the goalie and he comes closer as he tries to reduce my scoring angle. I'm left with only one option, to kick the ball over his head. It's not an easy move, but I'll try anyway. I get in my shooting position, and my right foot makes contact with both the grass and the ball, then...

9:00 am. The hip-hop of my alarm takes me from a great moment in soccer history, but I don't mind because today is a big day. After my shower, I wake my dad up, go to kitchen and eat one of my favorite meals, pasta. I'm ready an hour earlier than I need to be so I relax a little and wait for my dad because he's the one driving me.

We are both pretty quiet on the ride there. All we said to each other since waking up was, "Hi, good morning." It is a very sunny day and my mind is lost looking at the trees, the McDonalds that's two minutes away from my house, the clean cars all around us, and the people walking vaguely by. The silence is broken when my dad asks, "Do you know where you're going to be sleeping?" and then he unleashes a long list of questions and I can only answer some of them. It feels like I am taking a survey, and I can see that he is worrying a lot about me spending the night somewhere else.

As we get closer to my destination, my heart rate starts to increase. I feel like going home because I am not ready for this. After twenty-five minutes on the road, we arrive at a big campus that reminds me a lot of my school in Haiti. There is a big sign with white letters that says, "Welcome to Saint Joseph's College."

My dad's questions are finished but mine are just beginning: "Am I going to have fun? Am I going to see people I know? Am I going to be the only black person here?" It is time to say goodbye. "Give a call tonight before you go to bed," says my dad. We shake hands and then I watch him drive away from the campus. I walk into the nearest building, see one of my ex soccer teammates and begin my adventure. What a coincidence, in Haiti, I spent my whole life in a private Catholic school, and now I am about to have my first overnight visit at a college that seems very similar.

Five other soccer recruits are also here for an overnight visit. We talk to the coach for a little while and then the older players show us around the campus. I hadn't expected to have so much fun. I meet new people, see friends that I haven't seen for a long time, play some soccer, and enjoy every minute of my time on campus. It's unfortunate that the visit is for only one night because I leave the next day really wanting to go to St. Joseph's.

Five years ago, if someone had asked me if I wanted to live in the United States I would probably have said no, because I thought that it would be too hard to fit in to a new community, learn a new language, and make new friends. But now that I've done it I realize that it's not such a big deal.

A few weeks after my visit to St. Joseph's I receive a letter that says I have been accepted and that I have been awarded a merit scholarship. Some people don't understand how hard it might be for an immigrant like me to go to college after only a few years of learning English. I'm lucky to have this great opportunity. All of the hard work that I've done has given me good results, and in September, my dad and mom will drive me to campus again, this time to stay.

5

OUTDOOR ADVENTURES

EXPLORING UNCHARTED LAND
Lulu Rasor

The great explorer pushed her way through the thick green vines. She hacked and slashed her way through a thicket of foot-long, spear-like thorns, only to have to wade through a deep and wide muddy river. More than once she was nearly swept downstream. Once she stopped to rest on the other side, a thought hit her: she was the only one ever to set foot on this land. It was uncharted forest.

"Well," she said to the forest, "better get started."

She squished her way through the swamp-like land, reaching into her backpack for a flag to stick into the ground. She wanted to claim the land for Luluia, the country that she represented. Suddenly a voice drifted through the muggy air.

"Luluuuu, time for luuuuunch…" called the voice.

She jumped, dropping her flag.

"Drat," she muttered.

She picked up the flag and waded across the stream that separated the two parts of the forest. Then she climbed the ravine to her house. The uncharted land would have to stay that way until after lunch.

About the Author

Lulu is ten years old. Her favorite numbers are 2, 4, and 9 (never any in between). She suffers from the rare disease of seaweed-o-phobia (great fear of swimming in seaweed). She does, however, like to swim in pools or lakes. Lulu might be able to survive if she was sucked into a time warp without any books or chocolate. She might go mad though because she is both a bibliophile and chocoholic (both addictions are self-proscribed). She has a twin sister, Pie, who might have broken the world record for being Most Annoying. Those who think that Pie and Lulu are weird names: they're just nicknames. Our real names are a government secret.

CHECKING POTS
Maggie Fernald

Characters:
Daniel Turner, 40 (Bob's father)
Bob Turner, 17 (Daniel's son)

Setting:
Portland Harbor, in late August

Scene 2:
Daniel is on the boat, the Stacie, with Bob. He's just told Bob that he want to propose to his girlfriend Sophie. The boat is named after Bob's deceased mother. *Daniel is steering the boat, and Bob is on the tip looking down at the water.*

Bob:
I still don't like her. Please, please, don't do this, Dad. Can you really just forget Mom so soon?

Daniel:
Bob! I'll never forget Mom. Let's talk about this later.

Bob:
Did you already buy a ring?

Daniel:
Yeah. I hid it at home.

Bob:
Bob whispers:
No turning back now.

Daniel:
Hey, come help me lift up this trap?
Daniel cuts off the engine and walks over to the side of the boat and finds a buoy painted green and purple.

Bob:
Sure.
He has a really sour face and a grouchy attitude.

Daniel:
Look, Bob. I'll wait awhile before I ask her to marry me. And maybe you can have some one-on-one time with Sophie. I will only marry her with your approval. You are my only child and my number one priority.
Bob releases the angry look upon his face.

Bob:
I will appreciate it if you do what you say.

Daniel:
I swear that I will, son. *They give each other a smile and pursue pulling the lobster trap out of the dark sea.*

KAYAKING IN THE SHALLOWS
Mayele Alognon

The water around my kayak was green and I could see little fish swimming around, minding their own business and paying no attention to my anxiety or me. I was alone in the middle of the lake. I could see land but it was a long way away.

My hearing was not at its best: all the noises around me were ten times as loud as they were the minute before. I could almost hear the flapping of the wings of the birds above. I could hear a speedboat in the distance and fellow campers screaming from amusement. I imagined a large wave coming my way; my arms were exhausted. "Stay calm, stay calm!" I whispered to myself.

I closed my eyes. I needed to calm down. My tranquility was interrupted by the sound of another kayak crashing into mine, making me fall into the shallow water. I stood up quickly. It was my friend, Ellia. "Where'd ya go?" she asked.

"Uh, nowhere. I got lost!" I stared at her, wondering where the rest of the kayakers were and how they did not realize that we weren't with them.

"Yeah, I know. Now we're lost…together." We pulled our kayaks onto the shore with the setting sky behind us reflecting almost all the colors of the rainbow mixing into one big mess. We sat on the sand, eyeing the melting sky, waiting for the other kayakers to miss us.

CYCLING THROUGH THE SEASONS
Theo Dean

Snow.
Cold and hard,
Hot cocoa and fires.
Cats sleeping on top of a warm stove
And dogs sitting,
Staring at the winter whirl.
Snow angels
And the cold sting
Of a snowball down your back.

Mud.
Soft and thick,
Inviting birds and grass.
Small flowers
Peeking out of the muck.
Dogs running and splashing,
Mouths wide,
Tongues lolling in the wind.

Blueberries.
Bursting on the tongue,
Staining a child's mouth.
Paste over
A crisp bread,
In ice cream or pie.
Large and soft,
Almost purple.

SKIING ON TITCOMB
Elysia P. Roorbach

Wednesday was my first ski of 2012. My two friends, twins Phoebe and Isabelle, had rented their equipment and were struggling to get their boots into their skis. "Hey guys!" I called up from our van, a greenish-blue color and about as old as I am. I climbed out and hoisted my skis up on my shoulder. I was already wearing my boots; I always do.

"Hi, Elysia!" Isabelle shouted. Phoebe was still involved with her skis. My mom took out her Rolling Stone and started reading. I clomped over to my friends and tossed down my skis.

Phoebe was sucking on her hair and stuck it to her face so that it looked like a beard. "Nice beard, Phe," I said, giggling. This happens to her every time we ski, downhill or cross-country. Isabelle was bouncing up and down. "Are you nervous?" I shrugged. "Not really. We got really good last year."

Mary, the twins' mom, came out of the lodge with our badges and secured them to our coats. "Where's the instructor?" Isabelle asked. Two high school kids, goofing around and knocking each other over, came over and announced, "We're instructors." Mary smiled. "Maybe you guys will be the girls' instructors."

Isabelle leaned into me. "Oh, God, no. Not high school kids…oh, God, no." Just then Rick Hardy came out of the shed. He'd been our instructor the year before, along with a guy named Tom. We loved Tom; our moms loved Rick. "Hey girls!" Rick called. "You're with me today."

When we got to the top of the mountain, Rick

said, "How about this first run we'll just go down. Just to see where you're at, skiing wise. Want to go first, Elysia?" "Um, okay," I said, looking nervously at Phoebe, who tried to suppress a laugh.

I positioned my skis and started down on the Bunny, but quickly took the shortcut to the Beagle. I pulled my goggles down, the wind stinging my eyes and making my hair slap in my face. After a few seconds, I realized I was smiling.

Skiing was so much fun. Your problems you were having in life, your friends' problems that were weighing you down…they all seemed to evaporate. Melt into the snow before you, right before you skied over them. Skiing was a kind of adrenaline nothing else could give you. The sound of your skis skidding along the snow, the feeling whenever you came across a big hill—here goes nothing!

When I reached the bottom, I hockey-stopped and Phoebe came down right behind me. I leaned out of the way, because Phoebe is famous for not knowing how to stop. Once she actually went all the way past the lodge and ended up under a tractor. "I love skiing," she said. And then fell over. I couldn't agree more.

STROLLING SCARBOROUGH BEACH
Leah Desveaux

I remember walking down the long boardwalk to the sand. I could smell the sea and hear the waves and the seagulls even before I got to the beach.

I remember stepping on the layer of rocks under my feet before I got to the cold, salty water that I swallowed a lot of. The water has hardly any seaweed in it. I love the big waves that were perfect for boogie boarding and bodysurfing.

I remember getting out of the water and feeling the warm sand on my feet.

I remember sunbathing and looking for sand dollars and sea glass, but only finding things like dried seaweed and driftwood.

I remember packing up and ending a perfect day at Scarborough Beach.

CAMPING ON AN ISLAND
Max Lapointe

Rescue never came in this story of my time stranded on an island in the middle of Maine. I awoke on a beach. I was wet and cold, and as I stood up I saw I was on an island. It was a big island with a beach and a forest. The beach was in a crescent shaped lagoon with rocks just under the waves and a current pulling at anything trying to escape.

It would take me about a day to walk around it. I was wet and cold and it was getting dark so I needed a fire. I checked my pockets. There was absolutely nothing in them to start a fire. I was shivering and there was only an hour of light left in the sky.

I started to walk down the beach and there I saw a small boat. I ran to it and found an unfixable hole in its bottom, but it would make a good shelter if I flipped it over and propped it up. From the boat I saw a cave that was only visible right at the spot I was standing so I went to it with an armload of stuff I found in the boat: a fishing hook and line, a sharp knife, a metal pot, and a full water bottle.

I dropped the pot and when it landed on the ground it hit a rock and made a spark—it was flint! I found some dry grass and some small twigs and started a fire. I could feel the cold lifting away.

As I had gathered enough wood for the night, I decided I was going to try and fall asleep. The sky was a time bomb; it was dark and it was probably going to rain.

Boom! The bomb went off and it started to pour. I guess it was good and bad that it was raining, because it turned out that the water bottle wasn't full of water, it was gasoline. I wished I had known that when I was trying to start a fire but I could fill it with water after I washed it out really, really well. I put the gas into some large clamshells I found, and soon my water bottle was full.

The next day I went into the forest to look for food in the rain, because I was really hungry. Finally I found some berries. Normally I would have been hesitant about eating wild berries but I knew what they were the second they hit my tongue—they were raspberries.

The rain finally stopped and I went walking down the beach. I saw for the first time that someone else had been here because there was a fire pit that might have been about two days old. I kept going down the beach and saw a camp. No one was there as far as I could see, but there were my guns and my boat.

LIVING BY THE BEACH
Carter Williams

In August, my family goes to the family summerhouse in Phippsburg. Often we eat at an overpriced restaurant there called the Lobster House, which is the only restaurant in the area. What's ironic is that I don't think we have ever ordered lobster even once there. My dad would speak to us in French, which tended to turn into playing around with French accents, saying words like "hambooger," instead of "hamburger."

Salt air flows through our house's doors and windows left open day and night. Sand lumps are under all of the rugs from wet feet coming back from the beach and leaving grainy trails behind, slowly turning the house into a massive sandbox. The cleaning lady, who comes every once in a while, is too lazy to vacuum up the sand. She just sweeps it under the rug, like she has for years, causing an uneven walking surface, like living on the moon with small craters.

The bathrooms are festooned with wet bathing suits creating a pungent beach smell. The closets are littered with tired flip flops and sandals from years past, also contributing to the problem of sand in the house. Once, when I was little and the weather turned, I went through these closets, pushing aside every item a beachgoer would ever need, trying to find a winter coat and being unsuccessful. My mother has never thought to bring any warm clothes for the rare overcast day.

She spends most of her time there cooking and reading, while my father tools around with boats and commutes to work. My sister takes long walks with her iPod blaring to keep herself from dying of boredom. My parents hide the television there. They say there is no reason to have a television because there are so many things to do outside, and they are right.

BREATHING IN THE RAIN
Amira Alsammrai

I like to hang out outside.
But one time
I lived
In a room
With a window
I had to lean out of
To see a patch of sky.
I could always hear the children playing outside
But through that window I had
No sunlight and no sky.
I couldn't tell if it was day or night.
I felt like I was in a small bird's cage.

I remember one night
The clouds hugged each other
And the sky rained.
That night I hated to stay
Sitting in my room so I went out
To breathe the roses' perfume
And see the raindrops falling on the paper bark
Of trees washed from the hot season.

I could feel thin water flowing between my feet
And purifying me for a new sunrise.

Back inside the rain fell on my window
Making a beautiful voice
And mixing its steam with my breath.
That day I felt I was flying with the raindrops
And I saw the gardens and deserts
I saw farms I saw houses.
The rain is miracle of god.
After the rain eased I went to bed
To sleep and to wash my heart again with the rain.
I could still smell it. I loved it.

WATCHING BEES AT DUSK
Ezrah aka "Mr. Bankhead," Vy, Aranne, and Carlos from the East End School

My favorite picture is of the road because it looks kind
of pretty when it's dark and the light shines down really
bright and it has a pattern to it—dark tree, the road,
yellow light, the dark tree again.

All the bees together look
Like a patch of leaves
Their wings like glass
My body full of fear
The buzzing rings my eardrums
Faster the bees move

I see a beautiful, yellow orange sun.
The sun is setting, but nobody notices through the thick fog.
I look at the picture of the ocean and almost cry.

BIKING AT RANG POND
Emma Anghel

The curvy bike paths covered in tree roots travel
through the woods.
The wind conducts the trees,
Playing the melody of the forest,
Swaying back and forth to the beat.

I remember the earthy smell
And the wind splashing into my face
Whenever I biked down the peaceful paths.

I remember the two playgrounds drenched
with laughter,
The slides waiting to be used,
And the rusty swings waiting peacefully for their turn.

I remember the squeaky trolley,
Its gleaming metal handle hot from the sun.

I remember the green grass of the clearing
Where I liked to run around and play.

I remember the wobbly picnic tables,

And the small grills where juicy hamburgers cooked.

I remember the hot sand that was always
the perfect place
To lie down after you'd met with the underwater world
That looked so tempting
from the gleaming water above.

I remember how long the beach was.
Whenever I walked on it I could hear
the sound of the waves
Dropping almost at the pace of a lullaby.

HUNTING IN THE DEEP WOODS
Noah Williams

In Maine, there is an old adage: if you don't like the weather, wait five minutes.

I've been waiting for three hours, and it's still freezing cold out here. It's so cold, in fact, that every time I exhale, a little puff of steam comes out of my mouth and floats down on to the gun cradled in my lap. It stains a small patch of the barrel black with condensation. I'm breathing through my mouth because it's quieter, or at least seems quieter, than when I breathe through my nose. Deer are sensitive about these things.

The tiny beads of water on my rifle have frozen into hard little droplets. This is where moisture comes to die. It's an old gun, with lots of dings, and nicks, and scratches to prove that this isn't its first day afield. My grandfather carried it for some sixty years with him before me, and it killed lots of deer. Old guns are always better for days like these, especially when your spit freezes before it hits the ground.

I've met lots of real Maine people during my sixteen years here. Not like the way a politician meets "real people" though. I know farmers and lobstermen, carpenters and heating techs, and lots and lots of teachers. Maine farmers do not wear overalls, chew straw, and smile as they drive by on their shiny green tractors. They are tough men, and even tougher women. They work longer and harder in a day than most people do in a week. Their tractors are not gleaming mounds of GPS-guided steel, but clunky old Olivers held together with baling twine and patch welds. Lobstermen and fishermen are equally as tough, and maybe twice as hardy. They must run in sync with the weather, the tides, and work in blistering sun and bone-chilling fog.

Speaking of cold, the nine-hour hand-warmers have tapped out at four, and I'm starting to lose feeling in my fingers. My toes are long gone. As the sun comes up, the complete and utter silence changes to just plain silence. The movement of a small bird hopping through the pine tree overhead punctuates the nothingness.

To be a Mainer (and not the kind who descends in June and then beats a hasty retreat back to Florida come September) you have to be tough. You need this tolerance and stamina that I've yet to see anywhere else. It's not determined by race, or gender, occupation, or religion. The term "Mainer" is its own demographic group.

I pack it in. I can't take this any longer. Any exposed flesh on my body has gone from painfully cold to pleasantly warm and tingly. The sun creeps toward the treetops as I push through the dense grove of hemlocks, into scattered second-year beech cuts, and back onto the old logging road. As I come around the bend, another hunter hiking in waves to me.

"Any luck?" he says, huffing and puffing. I look at his fancy sunglasses, immaculate blaze-orange parka with a black camouflage print, the glittering rifle in his right hand, and then back to my beat up old 30-30 and I think of the two pairs of pants I'm wearing. For a split second, I wish we could trade places.

"Nothing yet, but I'm hopeful," I say.

The man shivers. "Jesus, it's cold out. I'm glad I wasn't here any earlier."

I just smile, and am grateful for this morning, for the cold, and for this meeting. More than anything I'm grateful for the place I am right here and now.

Authors

ABOUT THE
TELLING ROOM

The Telling Room is a nonprofit writing center in Portland, Maine, dedicated to the idea that children and young adults are natural storytellers. Focused on young writers ages 6 to 18, our programs seek to build confidence, strengthen literacy skills, and provide real audiences for our students' stories. We believe that the power of creative expression can change our communities and prepare youth for future success.

The stories and poems in this guide were developed in Telling Room programs during 2011-2012 at our Commercial Street location and in schools and communities throughout Maine.

ACKNOWLEDGMENTS

The Telling Room would like to thank the National Endowment for the Arts, Maine Arts Commission, and the Virginia Hodgkins Somers Foundation for their generous support of this project.

Editing and compilation by Molly McGrath.
Cover design and book layout by Ari Meil.
Cover and interior illustrations by Jay Sacher.